D0239213

Contents

Words ending le

Remember

The 'ul' sound at the end of two-syllable words is most often spelt le.
double   uncle

Try it

1 Read the clue and write the word that ends with le.

a) si_____ (easy)

b) wr_____ (crease)

c) si_____ (just one)

d) gr_____ (moan, complain)

e) tw_____ (glimmer)

f) st_____ (trip, stagger)

g) mu_____ (mutter)

h) sp_____ (shine)

i) tu_____ (fall over)

j) tr_____ (shake with fear)

2 Complete the words in each box. Then add some more words using the first syllables **bun_____**, **crum_____**, **tri_____** and **rum_____**.

ckle	dle	ble	ple	gle
pri_____	can_____	scram_____	sam_____	jun_____
chu_____	han_____	trou_____		an_____
_____	_____	_____	_____	_____
		_____	_____	

Read—cover—write

Read this sentence and remember it. Then cover it and write it underneath.

A single trickle of water tumbles down the side.

_____

Check your spellings with the answers on page 40. Test yourself, or get a friend to test you.

I can spell all the words on this page. ☐   I can spell two-syllable words that end with **le**. ☐

Double letters before le

Remember

A **long vowel** is followed by **one** consonant before le.   nee<u>d</u>le

A **short vowel** is followed by **two** consonants before le.

If there is only one consonant sound it is a double letter.   mi<u>dd</u>le

Try it

1 Write in a double letter or single letter to complete the word. Use the letter in brackets.

a) bu ____ le (b)   f) mar ____ le (b)   k) hum ____ le (b)   p) ea ____ le (g)

b) da ____ le (z)   g) gi ____ le (g)   l) ti ____ le (t)   q) a ____ le (p)

c) poo ____ le (d)   h) ju ____ le (g)   m) wri ____ le (g)   r) go ____ le (b)

d) bee ____ le (t)   i) squi ____ le (g)   n) wo ____ le (b)   s) noo ____ le (d)

e) peo ____ le (p)   j) pu ____ le (d)   o) mu ____ le (d)   t) stee ____ le (p)

2 Follow the double-letter patterns to spell more words ending with **le**.

a) dri**zz**le → si _____ → fi _____ → pu _____ → gu _____

b) scri**bb**le → ho _____ → dri _____ → squa _____ → pe _____

c) mi**dd**le → ri _____ → cu _____ → pa _____ → hu _____

d) ke**tt**le → ne _____ → ra _____ → ba _____ → se _____

Read–cover–write

Read this sentence and remember it. Then cover it and write it underneath.

People huddle in the drizzle and begin to grumble.

_____

Check your spellings with the answers on page 40. Test yourself, or get a friend to test you.

I can spell all the words on this page. ☐   I can spell **le** words with double letters. ☐

Double letters before other endings

Remember

Use the double consonant rule to help you spell two-syllable words with other endings.   s<u>u</u>per (long vowel)   s<u>u</u>pper (short vowel)

 Some consonants are never doubled.   se**v**en ne**v**er.

Try it

1 Use the rule to decide if these words need a double letter or a single letter.

a) ha____en (p)   f) ba____er (n)   k) co____on (t)   p) a____ow (r)

b) so____y (r)   g) po____en (l)   l) pi____ow (l)   q) jo____y (l)

c) sca____er (t)   h) per____on (s)   m) wai____er (t)   r) la____y (d)

d) sea____on (s)   i) spi____er (d)   n) bu____on (t)   s) mi____en (t)

e) ho____ow (l)   j) hi____en (d)   o) fro____en (z)   t) par____y (t)

2 Spell these words with double consonants. Choose the consonant from the orange box.

a) su____en   co____ee   be____ar   ro____er   **b c d f g h j**

b) te____is   fri____y   co____a   pu____et   **k l m n p q**

c) le____on   si____le   bo____om   ca____ot   **r s t v w x y z**

Read–cover–write

Read this sentence and remember it. Then cover it and write it underneath.

The lady pressed the button and waited for a moment.

_____

Check your spellings with the answers on page 40. Then test yourself, or get a friend to test you.

I can spell all the words on this page. ☐

I can spell two-syllable words with double and single letters. ☐

Words ending el, al and il

Remember

In some words an 'ul' ending is spelt el, al or il.   model   animal   April

Try it

1 Add the second syllable to these words.
Use an ending from the orange box.

nel   rel   sel   vel   wel

a) bar_____   c) no_____   e) ken_____   g) squir_____   i) tro_____

b) je_____   d) vo_____   f) mar_____   h) sho_____   j) tin_____

2 The missing words have an **el** ending. Complete the words.

a) the Channel t_____   c) a luggage la_____

b) a c_____ with two humps   d) a bath tow_____

3 Use a coloured pencil to write over the letters that spell the 'ul' sound.
Then copy each word into the correct box.

total   pupil   equal   April   local   petal
pencil   pedal   metal   capital   nostril   fossil

al endings	il endings

Read–cover–write

Read these sentences and remember them. Then cover them and write them underneath.

Scores are level. The final totals are equal.

_____

Check your spellings with the answers on page 40. Test yourself, or get a friend to test you.

I can spell all the words on this page. ☐   I can spell words with **el**, **al** and **il** endings. ☐

7

More word endings

Remember

Some endings are found on many words.
Endings are not always spelt as they sound.
vill**age**   fic**tion**   tar**get**

Try it

1 Follow the spelling patterns to spell more words with the same ending.

a) pres**ent** → par_____ → urg_____ → confid_____ → tal_____

b) import**ant** → eleph_____ → brilli_____ → pleas_____ → serv_____

c) mark**et** → plan_____ → helm_____ → trump_____ → secr_____

d) cott**age** → mess_____ → pass_____ → man _____ → pack_____

e) mount**ain** → curt_____ → barg_____ → capt_____ → cert_____

f) frac**tion** → men_____ → fric_____ → posi_____ → ra_____

2 Read the clue and write the word. Use the endings from question 1 to help you.

a) di_____ (far away)

b) fou_____ (a spray of water)

c) ta_____ (a pill)

d) voy_____ (trip)

e) j_____ (where two roads meet)

f) mo_____ (a minute)

g) da_____ (break, harm)

h) ca_____ (covers the floor)

Read–cover–write

Read this sentence and remember it. Then cover it and write it underneath.

It was an important moment for the captain.

_____

Check your spellings with the answers on page 41. Test yourself, or get a friend to test you.

I can spell all the words on this page. ☐   I can spell words with common endings. ☐

Topic words 1

Learn to spell the months of the year. Take the word apart and find the tricky bits.

Read and look.	Write it. Take the word apart.	Write it. Find the tricky bits.	Remember it. Cover it. Write it.	Check. ✓
January				
February				
March				
April				
May				
June				
July				
August				
September				
October				
November				
December				

Read–cover–write

Read each sentence and remember it. Then cover it and write it underneath.

We go on holiday in July, August or September.

_____

My birthday is in April. June's is in October.

_____

Adding **ed**

Remember

Use the rules 'drop the e' and 'double the last letter' to add **ed** to words.

close → clos**ed**   trip → tripp**ed**   moan → moan**ed**

Try it

1 Add **ed** to the words in the orange box. Write the new words into the correct box below.

work   laugh   step   wash   knit   race   fear   note   trap   giggle

Just add **ed**	Drop the **e**	Double the last letter

2 Use the rules to change these actions into the past tense.

a) walk _____ and talk _____

b) dart _____ and dash _____

c) slip _____ and slop _____

d) mumble _____ and grumble _____

e) open _____ and close _____

f) stop _____ and stare _____

g) thump _____ and thud _____

h) rage _____ and roar _____

Read–cover–write

Read this sentence and remember it. Then cover it and write it underneath.

I raced and grabbed the rope and climbed out.

_____

Check your spellings with the answers on page 41. Then test yourself, or get a friend to test you.

I can spell all the words on this page. ☐

I can use the rules to add **ed** to words in the past tense. ☐

Adding **ed** and **ing** to words ending y

Remember

If a word ends with a consonant and y, change the y to an i to add **ed**.
c<u>r</u>y → cr**ied**

If there is a vowel before the y just add **ed**.   pl<u>a</u>y → play**ed**

To add **ing**, just add **ing**.   cry → cry**ing**   play → play**ing**

Try it

1   Add **ed** to the words in brackets. Write the word.

a) I (try) _____.

b) He was (annoy) _____.

c) The case was (carry) _____.

d) We (hurry) _____ along.

e) Water was (spray) _____.

f) The room was (tidy) _____.

g) The eggs were (fry) _____.

h) The ship was (destroy) _____.

i) They were (marry) _____.

j) The mice (scurry) _____.

k) The plane was (delay) _____.

l) The letter was (copy) _____.

2   Add **ed** and **ing** to each of these words.

a) bully   _____ _____

b) worry   _____ _____

c) empty   _____ _____

d) copy   _____ _____

e) tidy   _____ _____

f) reply   _____ _____

g) steady   _____ _____

h) rely   _____ _____

Read–cover–write

Read this sentence and remember it. Then cover it and write it underneath.

The boy replied that he had tried.

_____

Check your spellings with the answers on page 41. Test yourself, or get a friend to test you.

I can spell all the words on this page. ☐   I can add **ed** and **ing** to verbs ending with y. ☐

Irregular past tense

Remember

Not all verbs use **ed** to change to the past tense.

I buy → I bought   I see → I saw   I sleep → I slept

Try it

1 Make pairs of present and past tense verbs. Use an ending from the orange box.

> ow   ew   ear   ore

a) gr ____ and gr ____

b) thr ____ and thr ____

c) w ____ and w ____

d) bl ____ and bl ____

e) kn ____ and kn ____

f) t ____ and t ____

2 Change one letter to put these verbs into the past tense.

a) write → w _____

b) draw → d _____

c) drink → d _____

d) drive → d _____

e) swim → s _____

f) begin → b _____

g) make → m _____

h) ring → r _____

i) spend → s _____

3 Complete these charts of present and past tense verbs.

Present	Past		Present	Past
speak			break	
creep			keep	
	thought			fought
	caught			taught

Read–cover–write

Read this sentence and remember it. Then cover it and write it underneath.

As the wind blew I thought I heard someone crying.

_____

Check your spellings with the answers on page 41. Test yourself, or get a friend to test you.

I can spell all the words on this page. ☐   I can spell irregular past tense verbs. ☐

Adding s and es

Remember

If a word ends with a consonant before the y, change y to i to add es.
t<u>ry</u> → tries

If there is a vowel before the y, just add s.   destr<u>oy</u> → destroys

Try it

1 Add s or es to the words in the orange box. Write the words in the correct box below.

watch   bully   replay   punch   copy   reply   argue   crash   annoy

Just add s	Just add es	Change y to i and add es

2 Write the plural of these words.

a) one circus, two _____

b) one trolley, two _____

c) one penny, two _____

d) one poppy, two _____

e) one princess, two _____

f) one puppy, two _____

g) one chimney, two _____

h) one cherry, two _____

Read–cover–write

Read this sentence and remember it. Then cover it and write it underneath.

Karl catches the butterflies as they land on the daisies.

_____

Check your spellings with the answers on page 42. Test yourself, or get a friend to test you.

I can spell all the words on this page. ☐   I can add s or es including words ending in y. ☐

Revision 1

1 Read the clue and write the word. Use an ending from the orange box.

el   il   le   al

a) d_____ (not single)

b) ba_____ (keep beer in it)

c) sh_____ (dig with it)

d) k_____ (a dog's house)

e) dr_____ (light rain)

f) wo_____ (shake like a jelly)

g) p_____ (part of a bike)

h) k_____ (boil water in it)

i) mu_____ (a mix up)

j) sq_____ (argue)

k) p_____ (draw with it)

l) t_____ (the sum)

2 Read the sentence. Write in the missing past tense verbs.

a) Jack th_____ the ball and I c_____ it.

b) I f_____ the bucket and Jack e_____ it.

c) Dad w_____ the dishes and I d_____ them.

d) Jamila h_____ the ladder as I cl_____ it.

e) Dad b_____ the gift and I wr_____ it.

f) Mum l_____ the key but I f_____ it.

g) The man a_____ a question and I r_____.

h) I t_____ a joke and everyone l_____ at it.

i) The teacher w_____ the word and we c_____ it down.

3 Check the spelling of the past tense verbs. Underline the word in each sentence that is wrong. Write the correct spelling.

a) She grabed a stick and struck the dragon. _____

b) I turned as a wizard appeard and waved his wand. _____

c) She lifted the latch and tride to get in. _____

d) He opend the box and smiled. _____

e) People cheered when my friends got marryed. _____

> Check your spellings with the answers on page 42.

Topic words 2

Learn to spell these words. Take the word apart and find the tricky bit. Use the empty rows for other words that you find tricky.

Read and look.	Write it. Take the word apart.	Write it. Find the tricky bit.	Remember it. Cover it. Write it.	Check. ✓
weight				
height				
straight				
multiply				
minute				
second				
metre				
triangle				
circle				
cylinder				

Read–cover–write

Read each sentence and remember it. Then cover it and write it underneath.

Find the height and weight of the cylinder.

_____

Draw a triangle in a circle in less than a minute.

_____

Spelling patterns: c and k

Remember

The 'k' sound is spelt **ck** after a short vowel and **k** after a long vowel or consonant.   st<u>i</u>**ck**   ch<u>o</u>**k**<u>e</u>

At the end of a two-syllable word it is often spelt **c**.   mu-si**c**

Try it

1 Add the correct 'k' spelling to these words.

a) wha____   d) topi____   g) plasti____   j) bul____

b) wre____   e) fre____les   h) picni____   k) strea____

c) comi____   f) brea____   i) hul____   l) sha____en

2 Read the clue and complete the missing word.

a) That's fan_____ news. (wonderful)   d) misty and mu_____ (gloomy)

b) "Don't p_____!" (be frightened)   e) snap, cr_____ and pop (crunch)

c) the ba_____ rules (main)   f) an el_____ band (stretchy)

3 All these words have **k** near the beginning. Add the missing letters.

Top tip Think about the letters that usually come before and after **k**.

a) k____che__   c) k__lo   e) __k__tch   g) __ki   i) __k____tl__

b) k__tt__n   d) k__tch__p f) __k____eton   h) __k__lled j) __ku__l

Read–cover–write

Read this sentence and remember it. Then cover it and write it underneath.

A plastic skeleton has a skull but no skin.

_____

Check your spellings with the answers on page 42. Then test yourself, or get a friend to test you.

I can spell all the words on this page. ☐

I can spell words with 'k' at the start, middle and end. ☐

Spelling patterns: x and ex

Remember

Very few words begin with **x** but lots begin with **ex**.

exclaim   expand   experience

Try it

1 Add the **ex** letter pattern to the beginning of these words.

a) ____ act   e) ____ ist   i) ____ am   m) ____ haust   q) ____ it

b) ____ pel   f) ____ pert   j) ____ plore   n) ____ press   r) ____ pect

c) ____ cite   g) ____ cept   k) ____ ceed   o) ____ cellent   s) ____ cuse

d) ____ tend   h) ____ tinct   l) ____ treme   p) ____ tract   t) ____ tra

2 Write in the missing letters or syllables to spell these words with **x** in them. The clues in brackets will help you.

a) r _ _ _ _ x (rest)

b) c _ _ _ _ _ _ _ x (not simple)

c) _ _ x _ _ _ (part of a graph)

d) _ _ xch _ _ _ _ _ _ (swap)

e) _ _ xp _ _ _ _ (make bigger)

f) _ _ xp _ _ _ _ _ _ (cost)

g) _ _ x _ _ _ ine (look at, inspect)

h) _ _ xper _ m _ _ _ _ (investigate in science)

i) _ _ _ _ _ _ x (list of key words in book)

j) _ _ xerc _ _ _ _ _ (workout)

k) _ _ xp _ _ _ _ _ _ (blow up)

l) _ _ xp _ _ _ _ _ _ (give reasons)

Read–cover–write

Read this sentence and remember it. Then cover it and write it underneath.

Can you explain why extra exercise is exhausting?

_____

More 'or' spellings

Remember

The main spellings of the 'or' sound are **or** and **aw**.   **sport**   **awkward**

But there are other spellings you need to learn.
war**d**   **A**u**g**ust   st**al**k   th**ough**t   there**f**ore

Try it

1 Add the correct spelling of the 'or' sound to complete these words.
Use **or**, **ar** or **au**.

a) sc____n

b) sc____ch

c) qu____ter

d) ____thor

e) w____drobe

f) m____ning

g) n____th

h) ____der

i) w____

j) l____d

k) w____m

l) w____ning

m) f____m

n) th____n

o) b____ing

p) sw____m

q) s____ce

r) rew____d

s) dinos____r

t) l____nch

2 Change the letters to spell more words with the 'or' sound.

Change:

a) cause – **c** to **p** → _____

b) yawn – **y** to **d** → _____

c) crawl – **cr** to **sh** → _____

d) chalk – **ch** to **st** → _____

e) thought – **th** to **f** → _____

Change:

f) haunt – **h** to **t** → _____

g) drawn – **d** to **p** → _____

h) scrawl – **l** to **ny** → _____

i) taught – **t** to **c** → _____

j) walk – **w** to **t** → _____

Read–cover–write

Read this sentence and remember it. Then cover it and write it underneath.

I thought I would crawl into the warm wardrobe.

_____

Check your spellings with the answers on page 43. Then test yourself, or get a friend to test you.

I can spell all the words on this page. ☐

I can choose the correct 'or' spelling in lots of words. ☐

More 'ur' spellings

Remember

The main spellings for the 'ur' sound in the middle of a word are **ur**, **ir** and **er**.   blur   dirt   fern

But there are other spellings you need to learn.   word   earn

Try it

1 Choose the correct spelling for each chain of words. Write in **ur**, **er**, **ir** or **or**.

a) ch____n → ____ge → sp____t → h____l → s____f

b) th____st → sm____k → f____m → wh____l → sw____l

c) w____k → w____se → w____ship → w____ld → w____thy

d) k____b → t____m → j____k → h____b → sw____ve

2 Write these words correctly.

a) mirmer _____   d) disterb _____   g) sirprise _____

b) thurty _____   e) perpose _____   h) firther _____

c) injere _____   f) cerve _____   i) purhaps _____

3 Write in the missing letters. Use **er** or **ear**.

a) ____th   c) n____ve   e) s____ve   g) ____ly   i) l____n

b) h____d   d) p____son   f) s____ch   h) p____l   j) v____b

Read–cover–write

Read this sentence and remember it. Then cover it and write it underneath.

Not a murmur to disturb the sleeping world.

_____

Check your spellings with the answers on page 43. Test yourself, or get a friend to test you.

I can spell all the words on this page. ☐   I can choose the correct 'ur' spelling in lots of words. ☐

More 'oo' and 'yoo' spellings

Remember

The main spellings for the 'oo' and 'yoo' sounds are **oo**, **ue**, **ew** and **u-e**.
scoot   blue   few   huge

But there are other spellings you need to learn.
cruise   move   super   group

Try it

1   Write in the letters to spell the missing 'oo'/'yoo' sound. Use **ue**, **u-e** or **ew**.

a) d____   d) stat____   g) tiss____   j) cost__m__   m) am__s__

b) resc____   e) arg____   h) n____s   k) val____   n) cr____l

c) st____   f) neph____   i) purs____   l) contin____   o) d__k__

2   Use a coloured pencil to write over the letters that spell the 'oo'/'yoo' sound. Then copy each word into the correct box.

fruit   shoe   prove   soup   view   unit
through   truth   bruise   lose   youth   juice

ui (cruise)	ou (group)	o-e (move)	u (super)	others

Read–cover–write

Read this sentence and remember it. Then cover it and write it underneath.

Can you drink soup and fruit juice through a straw?

_____

Check your spellings with the answers on page 43. Then test yourself, or get a friend to test you.

I can spell all the words on this page. ☐

I can choose the correct 'oo' or 'yoo' spelling in lots of words. ☐

Topic words 3

Learn to spell these words. Take the word apart and find the tricky bit.
Use the empty rows for other words that you find tricky.

Read and look.	Write it. Take the word apart.	Write it. Find the tricky bit.	Remember it. Cover it. Write it.	Check. ✓
tough				
quiet				
terrible				
pleasant				
weird				
peculiar				
ancient				
fierce				
favourite				
beautiful				

Read–cover–write

Read each sentence and remember it. Then cover it and write it underneath.

The favourite son was pleasant and gentle.

_____

The quiet night was broken by a terrible fierce roar.

_____

The meat was tough and tasted peculiar.

_____

Adding y

Remember

Use the rules 'drop the e' and 'double the last letter' to add y.
smoke → smoky   wobble → wobbly   fog → foggy

For other words, just add y.   rain → rainy

Try it

1 Change the words in the orange box into adjectives by adding y. Write the adjectives in the correct box below.

flake   thirst   flop   noise   mud   stick

water   nut   bounce   bone   crunch   knot

Just add y	Drop the e	Double the last letter

2 Choose five words from the orange box which you can add y to. Write the five describing words.

cuddle   sparkle   puddle   wriggle   wrinkle   dazzle   cobble   bubble

_____   _____   _____   _____   _____

Read–cover–write

Read this sentence and remember it. Then cover it and write it underneath.

The outside is crunchy and nutty and inside it's all runny.

_____

Check your spellings with the answers on page 43. Then test yourself, or get a friend to test you.

I can spell all the words on this page. ☐

I can use the rules to change words into adjectives by adding y. ☐

Adding er and est

Remember

Use the same rules for adding **er** and **est** as you use for adding **ed**.

Drop the **e**.   safe → saf**er**

Double the last letter.   big → bi**gg**est

Change **y** to **i**.   funny → funn**i**est

Try it

1   Use the rules to complete these comparison tables.

root word	+ er	+ est
smooth		
close		
flat		
large		
sad		

root word	+ er	+ est
thin		
cute		
tough		
fierce		
weird		

2   Add the suffix to the root word.

a) happy (er) _____

b) lucky (est) _____

c) pretty (est) _____

d) early (er) _____

e) hungry (est) _____

f) crazy (er) _____

Read–cover–write

Read this sentence and remember it. Then cover it and write it underneath.

It was the noisiest and craziest party ever.

_____

Check your spellings with the answers on page 44. Test yourself, or get a friend to test you.

I can spell all the words on this page. ☐   I can use the rules to add **er** and **est** to words. ☐

Adding ly

Remember

For most words, just add **ly**.   near → nearly   brave → bravely

For words that end **y**, change **y** to **i**.   merry → merrily

For words that end **le**, change **le** to **ly**.   simple → simply

Try it

1 Add the suffix **ly** to these root words and write the new word.

a) real _____   f) proud _____   k) safe _____

b) easy _____   g) happy _____   l) angry _____

c) quiet _____   h) wise _____   m) clumsy _____

d) fierce _____   i) quick _____   n) greedy _____

e) gentle _____   j) weary _____   o) sudden _____

2 Complete these words ending with **ly**. Use the clue to help you.

a) li_____ (alive, full of life)   f) fr_____ (nice, welcoming)

b) lo_____ (feeling alone)   g) li_____ (will probably happen)

c) mo_____ (every month)   h) ur_____ (without delay)

d) ne_____ (almost)   i) fi_____ (in the end)

e) lu_____ (with luck)   j) sli_____ (just a little)

Read–cover–write

Read this sentence and remember it. Then cover it and write it underneath.

She came home safely, happily and proudly.

_____

Check your spellings with the answers on page 44. Test yourself, or get a friend to test you.

I can spell all the words on this page. ☐   I can add **ly** to root words. ☐

Spelling words with suffixes

Remember

Finding the root word and recognising the suffix can help to spell lots of longer words.

faith/ful faith/less   drink/able   read/er   dark/ness

Try it

1 Write these words so you can see the root word and suffix.

a) youthful _____ _____   i) truthful _____ _____

b) peaceful _____ _____   j) tuneless _____ _____

c) breathless _____ _____   k) speechless _____ _____

d) breakable _____ _____   l) avoidable _____ _____

e) enjoyable _____ _____   m) frighten _____ _____

f) firmness _____ _____   n) gentleness _____ _____

g) quietness _____ _____   o) amazement _____ _____

h) movement _____ _____   p) amusement _____ _____

2 Use suffixes to build more words from these words. Write four words for each root word.

strange _____ _____ _____ _____

use _____ _____ _____ _____

Read–cover–write

Read this sentence and remember it. Then cover it and write it underneath.

All that movement left me breathless.

_____

Check your spellings with the answers on page 44. Test yourself, or get a friend to test you.

I can spell all the words on this page. ☐   I can spell words by adding suffixes to root words. ☐

Revision 2

1   **Read the clue and write the word. All the words end with a suffix.**

a) An elephant's skin is wri_____.

b) Ripe plums are ju_____.

c) A dull day is cl_____.

d) Hedgehogs are pri_____.

e) A ball is bou_____.

f) Drums are noi_____.

g) br_____ a_____ (can be broken)

h) spe_____ l_____ (lost for words)

i) tru_____ f_____ (honest)

j) bre_____ l_____ (panting)

k) am_____ m_____ (shock, surprise)

l) pe_____ f_____ (quiet and still)

2   **Read the sentence. Write in the missing words.**

a) A hill is big but a mountain is
    b_____.

b) A mouse is qu_____t but
    a butterfly is q_____.

c) An oven is h_____ but
    the sun is h_____.

d) This big load is he_____ but that
    one is the h_____.

e) The winners were ha_____
    and their fans even
    h_____.

3   **Check the spelling of words with suffixes. Underline the word in each sentence that is wrong. Write the correct spelling.**

a) The tiger moved quietly and slowly but growled fiercly. _____

b) The shorter, fatter elf was friendly and cuddley. _____

c) The stranger found the map realy useful. _____

d) Happily, the jolly farmer gave a cheerey wave. _____

> Check your spellings with the answers on page 44.

Topic words 4

Learn to spell these words. Take the word apart and find the tricky bit.
Use the empty rows for other words that you find tricky.

Read and look.	Write it. Take the word apart.	Write it. Find the tricky bit.	Remember it. Cover it. Write it.	Check. ✓
diet				
sugar				
heart				
young				
touch				
flavour				
breathe				
strength				
transparent				
bacteria				

Read–cover–write

Read each sentence and remember it. Then cover it and write it underneath.

Sugar adds flavour, but too much sugar in a diet is bad.

As I run, my heart beats faster and I breathe more quickly.

I tested the strength of the transparent plastic sheet.

Shortened forms 1

Remember

Shortened forms often follow pronouns. The apostrophe goes after the pronoun in the place of the missing letter or letters.

I had → I'd   I am → I'm

Try it

1   Write these shortened forms in the correct box.

I've   you've   you'll   he's   she's   he'll   we're   we've   they're   they'll

have → 've	will → 'll	is → 's	are → 're

2   Replace the full form with the shortened form.

a) I am _____ hungry.

b) I have _____ been there.

c) She will _____ be there.

d) They are _____ great.

e) You will _____ be there.

f) I will _____ see you then.

g) She is _____ late.

h) They have _____ missed the bus.

i) We will _____ be there.

j) Ajay is _____ following us.

Read—cover—write

Read this sentence and remember it. Then cover it and write it underneath.

I'm still waiting, but they'll be here soon.

_____

Check your spellings with the answers on page 45. Test yourself, or get a friend to test you.

I can spell all the words on this page. ☐   I can write shortened forms with apostrophes. ☐

28

Shortened forms 2

Remember

In contractions the apostrophe always goes in place of the missing letter or letters.   Do n(o)t → don't   are n(o)t → aren't   he (woul)d → he'd

Try it

1 Write the contraction next to the full form.

a) have not _____

b) I would _____

c) will not _____

d) what is _____

e) could not _____

f) you would _____

g) I had _____

h) where is _____

i) had not _____

j) would not _____

k) were not _____

l) shall not _____

2 Write the two examples in question 1 where the first word is also shortened. _____   _____

3 Replace the full forms in **bold** with contractions.

I have _____ got a problem. My car **will not** _____ start and I **have not** _____ a clue what to do. I **do not** _____ know **what is** _____ wrong. It just **does not** _____ want to start. **I would** _____ ask my neighbours but **they are** _____ away. **They would** _____ know what to do. If **I am** _____ late for work the boss **will not** _____ be pleased and **I will** _____ get the sack.

Read–cover–write

Read this sentence and remember it. Then cover it and write it underneath.

I know he won't like it but it doesn't matter.

_____

Check your spellings with the answers on page 45. Test yourself, or get a friend to test you.

I can spell all the words on this page. ☐   I can use apostrophes in contractions. ☐

Silent letters

Remember

Some words have letters you cannot hear.

knock clim**b** **w**rap **g**nat lis**t**en s**c**ene **h**our

Try it

1 Write in the silent letter to spell these words correctly.

a) whis __ le

b) __ reckage

c) glis __ en

d) __ nobbly

e) __ nome

f) num __

g) cas __ le

h) g __ ost

i) __ nuckle

j) dum __

k) __ onest

l) s __ issors

2 Read these words. Write over the silent letters. Write the words in the correct box.

rustle   sword   gnarled   answer   jostle   whole
sign   bristle   gnaw   bustle   wrestle   gnash

silent w	silent t	silent g

Read–cover–write

Read this sentence and remember it. Then cover it and write it underneath.

Listen for the whistle and give your answer.

_____

Check your spellings with the answers on page 45. Test yourself, or get a friend to test you.

I can spell all the words on this page. ☐   I can remember words with silent letters. ☐

Soft g and soft c

Remember

Sometimes a 'j' sound is spelt **g**.   **m**a**g**ic   **g**inger   stran**g**e

Sometimes a 's' sound is spelt **c**.   **c**entre   re**c**ipe   noti**c**e

Try it

1 These words all have a 'j' sound spelt **g**. Write the words correctly.

a) urjent _____

b) intellijent _____

c) jym _____

d) jenius _____

e) imajine _____

f) fidjet _____

g) rejister _____

h) dijest _____

i) anjel _____

j) jentle _____

k) jerbil _____

l) enjine _____

2 All these words have a 's' sound spelt **c**. Read the clue and write the word.

a) _____ tury (100 years)

b) par _____ (package)

c) de _____ e (make a choice)

d) ch _____ (a selection)

e) can _____ (call off)

f) _____ le (round shape)

g) su _____ ss (not failure)

h) re _____ (say a poem)

i) _____ ain (sure)

j) con _____ tr _____ (think, focus)

Read–cover–write

Read this sentence and remember it. Then cover it and write it underneath.

A recent urgent message warned of danger in the city.

_____

Check your spellings with the answers on page 45. Test yourself, or get a friend to test you.

I can spell all the words on this page. ☐   I can spell words with soft **g** and soft **c** spellings. ☐

Homophones

Remember

Some words sound the same but have different spellings and meanings. Use the correct spelling in the correct place.

Don't **break** anything.　　　**Brake** before we hit the wall!

Try it

1 Choose the correct word from the box to go in each space in the sentence.

a) He carried a _____ case onto the _____.　　**plane plain**

b) I _____ that summer is nearly _____.　　**here hear**

c) I will _____ a letter _____ away.　　**right write**

d) I _____ the left turn in the _____.　　**mist missed**

e) Have you _____ about the _____ of cows?　　**herd heard**

f) I _____ chop _____ if I could.　　**wood would**

g) It was _____ to see a fire in the _____.　　**great grate**

2 Add an extra letter to each of these words to make its homophone.

__rap　　　　__not　　　　__hole　　　　__new　　　　__night

Read–cover–write

Read this sentence and remember it. Then cover it and write it underneath.

I heard you had a great time on the plane.

_____

Check your spellings with the answers on page 46. Then test yourself, or get a friend to test you.

I can spell all the words on this page. ☐

I can choose the correct spelling of words that sound the same. ☐

Topic words 5

Learn to spell these words. Take the word apart and find the tricky bit.

Read and look.	Write it. Take the word apart.	Write it. Find the tricky bit.	Remember it. Cover it. Write it.	Check. ✓
scene				
narrator				
poem				
rhyme				
rhythm				
question				
character				
dictionary				
grammar				
sentence				
describe				

Read–cover–write

Read each sentence and remember it. Then cover it and write it underneath.

This scene needs a narrator and three characters.

_____

The poem has rhythm and rhyme.

_____

Check the grammar of your sentences when you describe the scene.

_____

Prefixes: re, de, pre and mis

Remember

When you add a prefix it changes the meaning of the word but not the spelling.   do → **re**do   mist → **de**mist   fix → **pre**fix   treat → **mis**treat

Try it

1 Add the prefix **mis** or **re** to these words to make new words.

a) _____ lead   e) _____ behave   i) _____ fire   m) _____ call

b) _____ load   f) _____ write   j) _____ visit   n) _____ heat

c) _____ turn   g) _____ trust   k) _____ hear   o) _____ chief

d) _____ move   h) _____ appear   l) _____ start   p) _____ fresh

2 Add prefixes to the words in the orange box to make new words. Write the new words in the correct box below. Some words can use more than one prefix.

paid   count   place   frost   cook   view   form   use   take   code

re (again or back)	de (undo it)	pre (before)	mis (wrong)

Read–cover–write

Read this sentence and remember it. Then cover it and write it underneath.

Replace the prefix and rewrite the word.

_____

Check your spellings with the answers on page 46. Test yourself, or get a friend to test you.

I can spell all the words on this page. ☐   I can spell words with prefixes. ☐

More prefixes

Remember

You can spell lots of longer words if you can spell the prefixes and root words.

re/charge   dis/miss   ex/change   anti/clockwise

Try it

1 Write each word so you can see the prefix and root word.

a) rebuild _____ _____

b) decrease _____ _____

c) nonsense _____ _____

d) misfortune _____ _____

e) disobey _____ _____

f) rebound _____ _____

g) misspell _____ _____

h) disable _____ _____

i) antiseptic _____ _____

j) disrepair _____ _____

k) undone _____ _____

l) regroup _____ _____

m) uncertain _____ _____

n) subheading _____ _____

2 Take these words apart. Write each word so you can see the parts.

a) misunderstand _____

b) unfriendly _____

c) disappointed _____

d) anticlockwise _____

e) disgraceful _____

f) unevenly _____

g) delighted _____

h) recovery _____

Read–cover–write

Read this sentence and remember it. Then cover it and write it underneath.

We are uncertain whether they can rebuild the display.

_____

Check your spellings with the answers on page 46. Test yourself, or get a friend to test you.

I can spell all the words on this page. ☐   I can spell words by adding prefixes to root words. ☐

35

Words ending **ture** and **sure**

Remember

A 'chuh' sound at the end of a word is often spelt **ture**.   fixture

A 'zhuh' sound at the end of a word is spelt **sure**.   closure

Try it

1 All these words end with a 'chuh' sound. Read the clue and write in the missing syllables.

a) adv_____t_____ (an exciting quest)

b) m_____t_____ (a bit of this and a bit of that)

c) f_____n_____t_____ (tables and chairs)

d) p_____t_____ (you draw this)

e) c_____t_____ (to catch someone)

f) t_____t_____ (the feel of something)

g) fut_____ (not the past)

h) l_____t_____ (a serious talk)

2 Choose the correct ending. Complete the words using **ture** or **sure**.

a) crea_____   d) fea_____   g) trea_____   j) na_____

b) plea_____   e) mois_____   h) frac_____   k) struc_____

c) mea_____   f) lei_____   i) punc_____   l) sculp_____

Read–cover–write

Read this sentence and remember it. Then cover it and write it underneath.

Measure the mixture as shown in the picture.

_____

Check your spellings with the answers on page 46. Test yourself, or get a friend to test you.

I can spell all the words on this page. ☐   I can spell words ending with **ture** and **sure**. ☐

Possessive apostrophes

Remember

Adding 's shows that something belongs to someone.

Jill's trainers – the trainers belong to Jill
the man's boots – the boots belong to the man

Try it

1 Rewrite the phrase in bold using an apostrophe to show who possesses each thing.

a) A **camel has a** hump. <u>camel's</u>

b) **Dad has a** hammer. _____

c) The **lady has a** hat. _____

d) The **dog has a** kennel. _____

e) The **boy has** freckles. _____

f) **Sam has** good news. _____

g) The **shop has a** sign. _____

h) **Amir has a** watch. _____

Top tip Never use **'s** to make a plural.

2 Check the use of apostrophes in these sentences. Underline the words that are wrong. Write them correctly.

a) The books cover is torn and so are the page's. _____ _____

b) This is Lees house but hes lost his key's. _____ _____ _____

c) The flats window's were left wide open. _____ _____

Read–cover–write

Read this sentence and remember it. Then cover it and write it underneath.

The boy's homework was left in his mother's car.

_____

Check your spellings with the answers on page 46. Test yourself, or get a friend to test you.

I can spell all the words on this page. ☐   I can use 's to show possession. ☐

Revision 3

1 Write the word. Use the clue to help you.

a) sc_____ (cut with them)

b) me_____ (find the length)

c) cre_____ (a living thing)

d) pic_____ (an image or drawing)

e) s_____e (part of a play)

f) tre_____ (riches)

g) ans_____ (not a question)

h) w_____le (you blow it)

i) gli_____ (gleam, sparkle)

j) __n_____ed (twisted, knotted)

2 Write in a synonym for the words in **bold**. It must be a word with a prefix.

a) First **take off** _____ the lid.

b) Do not **play up** _____ in class.

c) We must **change** _____ the broken window.

d) The spy had to **work out** _____ the message.

e) They were talking **rubbish** _____.

f) This spell will make you **vanish** _____.

3 Check the spelling in these sentences. Underline the two words in each sentence that are wrong. Write the correct spellings.

a) I wuld like to thank you for this suprise party. _____ _____

b) The crowd were very exited by a goal just before harf time.

   _____ _____

c) He was badly injered but is starting to improove. _____ _____

d) We herd the murmer of voices coming closer. _____ _____

e) We had xplored the castle erlier in the day. _____ _____

> Check your spellings with the answers on page 47.

Tricky words

Learn to spell these words. Say the sounds and find the tricky bit.
Use the empty rows for other words that you find tricky.

Read and look.	Write it. Say the sounds.	Write it. Find the tricky bit.	Remember it. Cover it. Write it.	Check. ✓
does				
busy				
used				
above				
special				
family				
through				
island				
often				
building				

Read–cover–write

Read each sentence and remember it. Then cover it and write it underneath.

The island is a special place for my family.

_____

The train often does go through the tunnel.

_____

Answers

Page 4

1
a) simple
b) wrinkle
c) single
d) grumble
e) twinkle
f) stumble
g) mumble
h) sparkle
i) tumble
j) tremble

2

ckle	dle	ble	ple	gle
prickle, chuckle, trickle	candle, handle, bundle	scramble, trouble, crumble, rumble	sample, crumple, triple, rumple	jungle, angle, bungle

Page 5

1
a) bubble
b) dazzle
c) poodle
d) beetle
e) people
f) marble
g) giggle
h) juggle
i) squiggle
j) puddle
k) humble
l) title
m) wriggle
n) wobble
o) muddle
p) eagle
q) apple
r) gobble
s) noodle
t) steeple

2
a) drizzle, sizzle, fizzle, puzzle, guzzle
b) scribble, hobble, dribble, squabble, pebble
c) middle, riddle, cuddle, paddle, huddle
d) kettle, nettle, rattle, battle, settle

Page 6

1
a) happen
b) sorry
c) scatter
d) season
e) hollow
f) banner
g) pollen
h) person
i) spider
j) hidden
k) cotton
l) pillow
m) waiter
n) button
o) frozen
p) arrow
q) jolly
r) lady
s) mitten
t) party

2
a) sudden   coffee   beggar   robber
b) tennis   frilly   comma   puppet (or punnet)
c) lesson   sizzle   bottom   carrot

Page 7

1
a) barrel
b) jewel
c) novel
d) vowel
e) kennel
f) marvel
g) squirrel
h) shovel
i) trowel
j) tinsel

2
a) tunnel   b) camel   c) label   d) towel

3

al endings	il endings
total, pedal, equal, metal, capital, local, petal	pencil, pupil, April, nostril, fossil

Page 8

1
a) present, parent, urgent, confident, talent
b) important, elephant, brilliant, pleasant, servant
c) market, planet, helmet, trumpet, secret
d) cottage, message, passage, manage, package
e) mountain, curtain, bargain, captain, certain
f) fraction, mention, friction, position, ration

2
a) distant
b) fountain
c) tablet
d) voyage
e) junction
f) moment
g) damage
h) carpet

Page 10

1

Just add **ed**	Drop the **e**	Double the last letter
worked, laughed, washed, feared	raced, noted, giggled	stepped, knitted, trapped

2
a) walked and talked
b) darted and dashed
c) slipped and slopped
d) mumbled and grumbled
e) opened and closed
f) stopped and stared
g) thumped and thudded
h) raged and roared

Page 11

1
a) tried
b) annoyed
c) carried
d) hurried
e) sprayed
f) tidied
g) fried
h) destroyed
i) married
j) scurried
k) delayed
l) copied

2
a) bullied, bullying
b) worried, worrying
c) emptied, emptying
d) copied, copying
e) tidied, tidying
f) replied, replying
g) steadied, steadying
h) relied, relying

Page 12

1
a) grow and grew
b) throw and threw
c) wear and wore
d) blow and blew
e) know and knew
f) tear and tore

2
a) write → wrote
b) draw → drew
c) drink → drank
d) drive → drove
e) swim → swam
f) begin → began
g) make → made
h) ring → rang
i) spend → spent

3

Present	Past	Present	Past
speak	spoke	break	broke
creep	crept	keep	kept
think	thought	fight	fought
catch	caught	teach	taught

Page 13

1

Just add **s**	Just add **es**	Change **y** to **i** and add **es**
replays, argues, annoys	watches, punches, crashes	bullies, copies, replies

2
a) circuses   e) princesses
b) trolleys   f) puppies
c) pennies   g) chimneys
d) poppies   h) cherries

Page 14

1
a) double   e) drizzle   i) muddle
b) barrel   f) wobble   j) squabble
c) shovel   g) pedal   k) pencil
d) kennel   h) kettle   l) total

2
a) Jack threw the ball and I caught it.
b) I filled the bucket and Jack emptied it.
c) Dad washed the dishes and I dried them.
d) Jamila held the ladder as I climbed it.
e) Dad bought the gift and I wrapped it.
f) Mum lost the key but I found it.
g) The man asked a question and I replied.
h) I told a joke and everyone laughed at it.
i) The teacher wrote the word and we copied it down.

3
a) She grabed a stick and struck the dragon. grabbed
b) I turned as a wizard appeard and waved his wand. appeared
c) She lifted the latch and tride to get in. tried
d) He opend the box and smiled. opened
e) People cheered when my friends got marryed. married

Page 16

1
a) whack   d) topic   g) plastic   j) bulk
b) wreck   e) freckles   h) picnic   k) streak
c) comic   f) break   i) hulk   l) shaken

2
a) fantastic   c) basic   e) crackle
b) panic   d) murky   f) elastic

3
a) kitchen   c) kilo   e) sketch   g) ski   i) skittle
b) kitten   d) ketchup   f) skeleton   h) skilled   j) skull

Page 17

1
a) exact   e) exist   i) exam   m) exhaust   q) exit
b) expel   f) expert   j) explore   n) express   r) expect
c) excite   g) except   k) exceed   l) extreme   s) excuse
d) extend   h) extinct   l) extreme   p) extract   t) extra

2
a) relax
b) complex
c) axis (or axes)
d) exchange
e) expand
f) expense
g) examine
h) experiment
i) index
j) exercise
k) explode
l) explain

Page 18

1
a) scorn
b) scorch
c) quarter
d) author
e) wardrobe
f) morning
g) north
h) order
i) war
j) lord (or laud)
k) warm
l) warning
m) form
n) thorn
o) boring
p) swarm
q) sauce
r) reward
s) dinosaur
t) launch

2
a) cause → pause
b) yawn → dawn
c) crawl → shawl
d) chalk → stalk
e) thought → fought
f) haunt → taunt
g) drawn → prawn
h) scrawl → scrawny
i) taught → caught
j) walk → talk

Page 19

1
a) churn → urge → spurt → hurl → surf
b) thirst → smirk → firm → whirl → swirl
c) work → worse → worship → world → worthy
d) kerb → term → jerk → herb → swerve

2
a) murmur
b) thirty
c) injure
d) disturb
e) purpose
f) curve (or serve)
g) surprise
h) further
i) perhaps

3
a) earth
b) heard (or herd)
c) nerve
d) person
e) serve
f) search
g) early
h) pearl
i) learn
j) verb

Page 20

1
a) dew/due
b) rescue
c) stew
d) statue
e) argue
f) nephew
g) tissue
h) news
i) pursue
j) costume
k) value
l) continue
m) amuse
n) cruel
o) duke

2

ui (cruise)	ou (group)	o-e (move)	u (super)	others
fruit, bruise, juice	through, soup, youth	prove, lose	truth, unit	shoe, view

Page 22

1

Just add y	Drop the e	Double the last letter
thirsty, sticky, watery, crunchy	flaky, noisy, bouncy, bony	floppy, muddy, nutty, knotty

2 cuddly, sparkly, wriggly, wrinkly, bubbly

Page 23

1

root word	+ er	+ est	root word	+ er	+ est
smooth	smoother	smoothest	thin	thinner	thinnest
close	closer	closest	cute	cuter	cutest
flat	flatter	flattest	tough	tougher	toughest
large	larger	largest	fierce	fiercer	fiercest
sad	sadder	saddest	weird	weirder	weirdest

2
a) happier
b) luckiest
c) prettiest
d) earlier
e) hungriest
f) crazier

Page 24

1
a) really
b) easily
c) quietly
d) fiercely
e) gently
f) proudly
g) happily
h) wisely
i) quickly
j) wearily
k) safely
l) angrily
m) clumsily
n) greedily
o) suddenly

2
a) lively
b) lonely
c) monthly
d) nearly
e) luckily
f) friendly
g) likely
h) urgently
i) finally
j) slightly

Page 25

1
a) youth ful
b) peace ful
c) breath less
d) break able
e) enjoy able
f) firm ness
g) quiet ness
h) move ment
i) truth ful
j) tune less
k) speech less
l) avoid able
m) fright en
n) gentle ness
o) amaze ment
p) amuse ment

2
These are just some examples. There are other possibilities.
strange – strangeness, strangely, stranger, strangest
use – useless, useful, user, useable

Page 26

1
a) wrinkly (or wrinkled)
b) juicy
c) cloudy
d) prickly
e) bouncy
f) noisy
g) breakable
h) speechless
i) truthful
j) breathless
k) amazement
l) peaceful

2
a) A hill is big but a mountain is bigger.
b) A mouse is quiet but a butterfly is quieter.
c) An oven is hot but the sun is hotter.
d) This load is heavy but that is the heavier (or heaviest).
e) The winners were happy and their fans even happier.

3 a) The tiger moved quietly and slowly but growled <u>fiercly</u>. fiercely
b) The shorter, fatter elf was friendly and <u>cuddley</u>. cuddly
c) The stranger found the map <u>realy</u> useful. really
d) Happily, the jolly farmer gave a <u>cheerey</u> wave. cheery

Page 28

1

have → 've	will → 'll	is → 's	are → 're
I've you've we've	you'll he'll they'll	he's she's	we're they're

2 a) I'm hungry. f) I'll see you then.
b) I've been there. g) She's late.
c) She'll be there. h) They've missed the bus.
d) They're great. i) We'll be there.
e) You'll be there. j) Ajay's following us.

Page 29

1 a) haven't d) what's g) I'd j) wouldn't
b) I'd e) couldn't h) where's k) weren't
c) won't f) you'd i) hadn't l) shan't

2 won't, shan't

3 [I have] <u>I've</u> got a problem. My car [will not] <u>won't</u> start and I [have not] <u>haven't</u> a clue what to do. I [do not] <u>don't</u> know [what is] <u>what's</u> wrong. It just [does not] <u>doesn't</u> want to start. [I would] <u>I'd</u> ask my neighbours but [they are] <u>they're</u> away. [They would] <u>They'd</u> know what to do. If [I am] <u>I'm</u> late for work the boss [will not] <u>won't</u> be pleased and [I will] <u>I'll</u> get the sack.

age 30

a) whistle d) knobbly g) castle j) dumb
b) wreckage e) gnome h) ghost k) honest
c) glisten f) numb i) knuckle l) scissors

silent w	silent t	silent g
sword, answer, wrestle, whole	rustle, bristle, bustle, jostle, wrestle	sign, gnarled, gnaw, gnash

31

) urgent d) genius g) register j) gentle
) intelligent e) imagine h) digest k) gerbil
) gym f) fidget i) angel l) engine

a) century f) circle
b) parcel g) success
c) decide h) recite
d) choice i) certain
e) cancel j) concentrate

Page 32

1
a) He carried a <u>plain</u> case onto the <u>plane</u>.
b) I <u>hear</u> that summer is nearly <u>here</u>.
c) I will <u>write</u> a letter <u>right</u> away.
d) I <u>missed</u> the left turn in the <u>mist</u>.
e) Have you <u>heard</u> about the <u>herd</u> of cows?
f) I <u>would</u> chop <u>wood</u> if I could.
g) It was <u>great</u> to see a fire in the <u>grate</u>.

2
rap → wrap, not → knot, hole → whole, new → knew, night → knight

Page 34

1
a) mislead
b) reload
c) return
d) remove
e) misbehave
f) rewrite
g) mistrust
h) reappear
i) misfire
j) revisit
k) mishear
l) restart
m) recall
n) reheat
o) mischief
p) refresh

2

re (again or back)	de (undo it)	pre (before)	mis (wrong)
repaid, recount, replace, review, reform, reuse, retake	defrost, deform, decode	prepaid, precook, preview	miscount, misplace, misuse, mistake

Page 35

1
a) re build
b) de crease
c) non sense
d) mis fortune
e) dis obey
f) re bound
g) mis spell
h) dis able
i) anti septic
j) dis repair
k) un done
l) re group
m) un certain
n) sub heading

2
a) mis under stand
b) un friend ly
c) dis appoint ed
d) anti clock wise
e) dis grace ful
f) un even ly
g) de light ed
h) re cover y

Page 36

1
a) adventure
b) mixture
c) furniture
d) picture
e) capture
f) texture
g) future
h) lecture

2
a) creature
b) pleasure
c) measure
d) feature
e) moisture
f) leisure
g) treasure
h) fracture
i) puncture
j) nature
k) structure
l) sculpture

Page 37

1
a) camel's
b) Dad's
c) lady's
d) dog's
e) boy's
f) Sam's
g) shop's
h) Amir's

2
a) The book's cover is torn and so are the pages.
b) This is Lee's house but he's lost his keys.
c) The flat's windows were left wide open.